This book was devised and produced by
Multimedia Publications (UK) Ltd.

Editor: Richard Rosenfeld
Assistant Editor: Sydney Francis
Production: Arnon Orbach
Design: Michael Hodson
Picture Research: Anne Lyons

First published in the United States of America 1985 by Gallery Books, an
imprint of W.H. Smith Publishers Inc., 112 Madison Avenue, New York,
NY 10016

ISBN 0 8317 2409 9

Origination by D S Colour International Ltd, London
Printed in Spain by Cayfosa, Barcelona
Dep. Leg. B-13715-1985

DOLPHINS

Endpapers: *A pair of common dolphins surfing on a wave.*

Above: *Dolphins proving that they can leap out of the water up to heights of 20 ft (6 m).*

Over: *A Pacific bottle-nosed dolphin opening his beak-like mouth to reveal rows of sharp teeth.*

Contents: *Dolphins appear to have a language of their own. They use sound not only as a means of communication but also as an aid to navigation in a world where vision is often limited.*

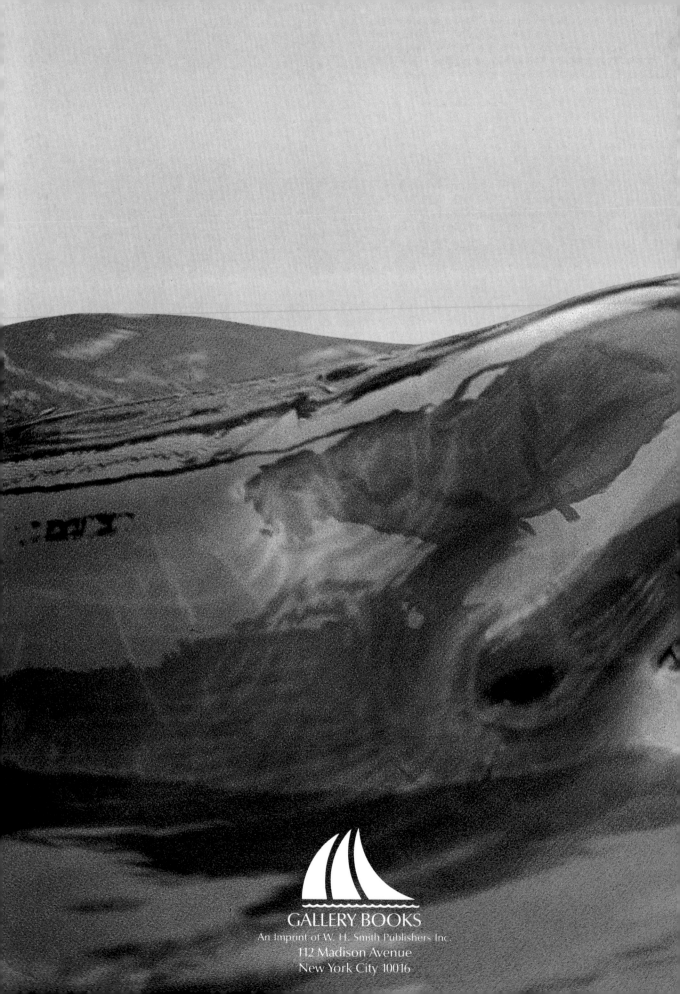

GALLERY BOOKS
An Imprint of W. H. Smith Publishers Inc.
112 Madison Avenue
New York City 10016

DOLPHINS

MICHAEL BRIGHT

Contents

Chapter 1
Dolphin Intelligence

"**W**henever I go into the water, he joins me. He slaps his flippers on the surface as a hello and then dances around me, diving down, spiraling, brushing against my legs.

"The first time he nosed his way under me, lifted me onto his back and took me for a ride I was scared, but only for a moment. He was so big. But he went slowly and was very gentle with me. Now those rides are my happiest moments. There's nothing like it. I hold onto his fin and we're off."

So wrote a 13 year old boy who lived in New Zealand. Dolphins, or porpoises as they are often called, inhabit nearly all the seas of the world, and there are river varieties too. Highly intelligent, they have worked their way into men's hearts from the times of the Ancient Greeks onwards. Of all the stories that exist, never has a dolphin been known to harm a man and many a time has he helped sailors in distress, fishermen in trouble or swimmers who have lost their way. Some claim dolphins have ESP and can telepathically understand a man's thoughts and moods. Perhaps this notion is romantic but certainly there is an affinity between man and dolphins and the more we come to know about our water cousins the more extraordinary they seem.

Sound and language

Dolphins have large brains and a highly folded cerebral cortex, not dissimilar to man's. It is generally thought that the bulk of the dolphin's brain power is assigned to the processing of acoustic information, for in dolphins the auditory sense has been developed into an incredibly sophisticated and effective sensory and communication system.

Sound is very important to dolphins. Under the sea, where vision may be restricted, sound is a good way of communicating and dolphins have a varied repertoire. They make squeaks, whistles, burps, groans, clicks, barks, rattles, chirps and moans. There have even been suggestions that emotional outbursts can be read into sounds.

Abrupt, loud sounds, often accompanied by jaw-clapping and tail-slapping are attributed to an angry dolphin, whereas intimate chuckles are heard during bouts of caressing and touching. Whistles seem to be identification signals, each individual having his or her own particular tune.

But dolphin sounds are clearly more than just signals or outbursts of emotion. Some researchers believe that

Dolphins are so keen to make contact with humans that they'll even pop out of the water for a quick scratch.

dolphins exchange information in a kind of language sometimes known as *delphinese*. In one famous experiment an American researcher placed a pair of bottlenose dolphins in separate tanks in such a way that they could hear but not see each other. Over a period of time

Dolphins are actually small toothed whales known as odontocetes. Their close relatives include killer and pilot whales, sperm whales, belugas and narwhals. Dolphins are small by whale standards, most being less than 15 feet (4.5m) long. Many species, like those shown above *and* right, *have a beak-like snout with rows of sharp backward-pointing teeth in a mouth that seems to wear a perpetual grin. One set of teeth lasts a dolphin for life, and they are well designed for grasping prey, such as squid or fish. Above and behind the snout is the bulbous* melon, *and on top of the head is the blowhole through which a dolphin breathes. Unlike fish, dolphins are marine mammals that need to come to the surface of the sea in order to breathe.*

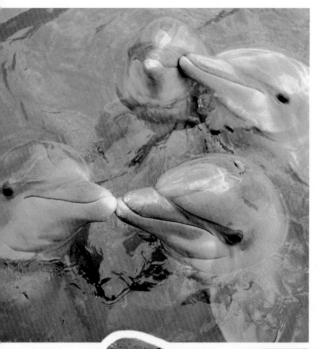

the female was taught to press one of a set of plungers to receive a reward. The male was presented with a similar bank of plungers but had no training. Nevertheless the male learned very quickly to push the correct plunger and the only way he could have received any relevant information was from the female. Throughout the tests the dolphins were heard to emit lots of squeaks, burps and clicks as if in deep conversation. The tests were not conclusive for the male might have worked the whole thing out for himself. However, if that was the case, that in itself would have been an amazing feat.

Learning a language

There are currently three American research programs in progress, all aimed at teaching captive bottle-nosed dolphins a man-made language. Much work has already been carried out with chimps and gorillas, and so far the ape level of naming and syntax, using gestural language, is equivalent to that of a two-and-a-half year old child. However dolphins are proving to be fast learners, can understand three-word sentences and have surpassed chimps in syntax. Soviet scientists found the intelligence of bottle-nosed dolphins to be on a developmental level equivalent to four to seven year olds!

The owner of the Delphinid Research Institute in Florida Keys is confident that one day dolphins will be able to respond to a spoken human language. At present his team of researchers is using whistles of differing pitch and duration to get dolphins to carry out complicated tasks. In just one year the dolphins have learned a fifty word "vocabulary" by this method — far more than a human child learns in its first year.

More ambitious scientists, armed with computers and associated electronic wizardry, are trying to find a way of letting dolphins talk back. At present there are many obstacles. For example dolphins speak about ten times faster than we do and at a much higher pitch. It is intriguing to consider whether they also think much faster than us as well. Perhaps one day the computer can bridge the gap for us.

Echolocation

Dolphins also make very high-frequency click sounds that are used mainly for finding their way through the sea or for detecting prey. A dolphin school will advance in a line, traveling abreast of one another and scanning

Dolphins in captivity (left) *and in the wild* (below) *have a curious affection for man. Some researchers suggest that dolphins are the most intelligent creatures on the planet, apart from man and his primate relatives. In dolphinaria they have proved to be perfect mimics, have phenomenal memories and sometimes invent their own routines and games. They constantly "speak" to each other, for sound communication is probably the most important factor in keeping a group of dolphins together, and coordinate the movements of each individual when the group goes hunting. In dolphin research programs scientists are attempting to understand their "language", hoping that one day it may even be possible to talk directly with them.*

the sea ahead with the ultrasounds they produce. This scanning system is called *echolocation*, and works when particular sounds emitted by the dolphins are bounced off objects in the water. The way the sounds are made is not fully understood but the principle has long been recognized. The use of radar in air travel guides aircraft in much the same way, and modern medicine relies heavily on ultrasound scanning techniques for "seeing" what the eye cannot see.

Dolphins breathe oxygen from the air through their blowholes, which are then closed for underwater swimming. The air can be shunted back and forth through a complicated "plumbing" system, with vibrat-

ing flaps and resonating chambers, to produce the very high-frequency sounds. These are emitted, not via the mouth, but through the forehead. At the front of a dolphin's head is the large bulbous structure known as the *melon*. Within it are specialized fats which serve to focus the sounds about a meter in front of the dolphin's head rather as a camera lens focuses light.

A narrow sound beam is produced that can be directed at objects in the dolphin's path. Sounds bounce back and are picked up, not by external ears but by the lower jaw. The returning signal is then transferred along more fatty tissue in the jaw to the ear, converted into nerve impulses and then analyzed in the brain. It

Divers who have been swimming with dolphins describe a faint tingling sensation on the back of the neck when an animal passes. It is thought that this is caused by a high intensity sound beam: the dolphins are "spraying" the diver with sound to find out more about him.

In tests dolphins are able to distinguish between identically shaped and colored objects made of different types of metal, or discriminate between a living and a dead fish – and all by using sound.

can tell the dolphin about obstacles to be avoided or food to be pursued. This unusual system enables dolphins to "see" with sound. Indeed, researchers have found that dolphins wearing rubber suction cups over their eyes to blindfold them can still easily find their way about and have no difficulty in locating food which has been thrown into their pool.

"Zapping" prey

Extraordinary as this facility is, what is equally surprising is the intensity of the sound. Dolphin researchers have found that when the dolphin is making its loudest sounds, say to pick up the location of distant objects, if the sound were any louder it would turn to heat. The dolphin is using its echolocation system to the absolute physical limit. And what is even more remarkable is the suggestion by some researchers that the dolphin can use this high-intensity beam of sound to "zap" its prey. Scientists have watched dolphins chasing schools of fish and have seen that the fish become disoriented. They think that the dolphins "spray" a fish school with sound, knock them out or perhaps even kill them with the sound beam, and are then able to scoop them up with comparative ease.

Another element of dolphin life which intrigued observers was the fact that dolphins never seem to zap one another, even by accident. With such a dangerous weapon in their heads they could easily cause injury

Left: *A group of common dolphins "running" during a hunt. Their prey is a dense school of juvenile fish* (above). *The dolphins encircle the fish, "spray" them with sound and then cut across the school gobbling the fish at will. The small fish, whether incapacitated by sound or simply exhausted from the chase, do not attempt to escape. Large salmon have been seen similarly to stop in their tracks when pursued by killer whales off Vancouver.*

unintentionally. It appears that they have evolved what could be called "echolocation manners". If a dolphin is actively echolocating and another approaches in front, the first dolphin will switch off its beam, wait for the other to pass and then switch it back on again.

Strandings

Occasionally, large numbers of dolphins are stranded on beaches, where they die from over-exposure to the sun. It is strange that an intelligent creature should get itself into such a position. Many scientists have tried to guess at an explanation. Some think that parasites in the ear and balance organs upset the dolphin's ability to find its way. Others suggest that, in the turbid water off a beach or mud-bank, a dolphin cannot see where it is going: its echolocation system doesn't work very well on soft sand or mud. When it finds itself suddenly in very shallow water the dolphin panics and continually swims

onto the shore even when returned to the water by frustrated human helpers.

There is, however, another intriguing theory that involves magnetism. A British researcher analyzed the records of dead or stranded dolphins and whales around the coasts of the British Isles and found that all the isolated cases of dolphins that had washed up on the shore, probably dead due to natural causes, belonged to species that normally lived close to land. However, the mass strandings nearly always involved those species that live habitually offshore.

Left: White-beaked dolphins near the Outer Hebrides in the north-western Atlantic Ocean, and (below) *a common dolphin with its young in the Java Sea. The white-beaked dolphin is a cold water species with a thick layer of blubber. It feeds very often on squid and so gained the name of "squid-hound" from Newfoundland fishermen.*

Other research work has shown that dolphins have particles of magnetite in the head and that these particles, surrounded as they are by a network of nerves, may sense the earth's magnetic field so giving the dolphin an idea of where it is at any one time. Other creatures like bees, pigeons, chitons, salamanders and even man have magnetite present and it has been shown that changes in the magnetic field can influence the direction in which they travel, as happens, for instance, during migrations. Perhaps the stranded dolphins had been swimming nonchalantly along with the echolocation systems switched off, guided by a kind of magnetic sense autopilot, when they hit a "magnetic valley" — a place where the earth's magnetic field is distorted — and became temporarily disoriented.

Scientists are able to measure the land's magnetic field and it has been found that the places where mass strandings most frequently occur do indeed coincide with magnetic valleys. Inshore species would be more diligent about where they are heading, confronted as they are by the enormous variety of obstacles along a coastline. Their offshore relatives, with the open, featureless ocean in which to roam, might not be so careful and so are caught "napping".

Dolphins on the move, "breaching" (left) and "running" (below). Even in the open ocean they must beware of obstacles. The World Wildlife Fund estimates that 10 000 Dall's porpoises are drowned each year after becoming trapped in lost and discarded fishing tackle that floats in the upper layers of the sea, as the new plastic filaments are invisible to the dolphin's sonar system. Monofilament nets, put down for the illegal netting of salmon, are another serious threat to dolphins and porpoises.

Social behavior and reproduction

Many species of dolphins live in large groups and have daily social routines. Hawaiian spinner dolphins, known for their ability to leap from the water and spin rapidly on their long axes, spend the best part of the day close to the shore, apparently resting. They feed at night and do not become active until late afternoon when individuals are seen to leap out of the water and splash about. This seems to be a signal for the rest of the school to rise and shine. The rushing about gradually gets more frantic. It is as if the group is having a roster-call, and that a check is being made on all the individuals in the school to ensure that they are ready to go hunting. The dolphins swim rapidly backwards and forwards until, at an unknown signal, they all turn tail and head out to sea.

Dusky dolphins, on the other hand, hunt during the day. They spend the night in small groups close to the shore, swimming slowly at about 3 mph (5 km/h), keeping a lookout for killer whales, their main predator. As many as 400 individuals may be living in an area only 10 miles (16 km) in diameter, but they start their hunting at dawn in smaller groups of up to 30 dolphins.

Pacific bottle-nosed dolphins (below) *"running" or "porpoising" off the Galapagos Islands. They are an inshore species, rarely seen more than 500 miles (800 km) from land, and often in the company of other whales, such as humpbacks and pilot whales. They appear to have a set foraging area or home range, and do not wander at random through the ocean. Several sub-groups of 10 to 20 animals come together on occasions for cooperative feeding, forming large herds of 500 individuals.*

Right: *Dolphins are such fast swimmers that they can reach speeds of up to 20 mph (32 km/h).*

24

Each group fans out in a line, scanning the sea ahead for fish shoals. Occasionally, dolphins will leap effortlessly as much as 20 ft (6 m) from the water in order to spot the flocks of seabirds that accompany and feed upon the fish shoals and, with an arched back, re-enter head first, cutting cleanly into the water. Having located the prey the dolphins perform noisy leaps in which they land back in the water on their side or with a belly-flop.

In this way they herd the fish and drive them towards the surface, acting like a wall and preventing them from escaping. The splashing also brings several dolphin groups together. Whether this is accidental or intended cooperative behavior is not known. Having finished feeding, the dolphins perform amazing acrobatic leaps, with spins and somersaults. This is thought to be another roll-call to bring the groups together again before they retire to the inshore waters for the night.

Some dolphins have been found to team up with other species. Tropical deep water races of the spinner dolphin associate with bridled or spotted dolphins. They live far from land and must be on a constant look-out for oceanic sharks. At night the spinner dolphins are actively hunting and therefore alert to danger, whereas during the day the bridled dolphins take their turn. The combined schools can be enormous with up to 10 000 animals traveling together many thousands of miles across the ocean.

Just as individual whales can be recognized by the markings on their flippers and tail, so too can dolphins be identified by tears along the trailing edge of the dorsal fin. By photographing dolphin schools, researchers have begun to work out group structure and composition. In some species, for example, there may be 15 dolphins swimming together but only five of them stay with that group constantly. The other 10 move around from group to group.

Left: *A dusky dolphin "breaching" at Peninsula Valdés.*
Above: *Pacific bottle-nosed dolphins at Monterey Bay,
California.* Below: *Common dolphins "porpoising".*

    If a member of a dolphin school is injured or in any kind
of distress, the others will often show concern. They may,
for instance, get very excited, swimming rapidly in circles,
biting any lines or nets, or ramming boats. If an animal is
injured and unable to swim the rest of the group will gather
around and support it so that the blowhole is kept above the
surface of the sea. There are reports of dolphins rendering
the same help to humans: a 20 year old Pretoria girl was
saved by dolphins in Delagoa Bay, Mozambique, when she
was being pursued by four sharks.

Contrary to popular belief, dolphins can be very aggressive. In some species fighting, when one dolphin might scrape its teeth along the body of another, establishes a dominant hierarchy, although an open mouth directed at a subordinate animal can be sufficient to bring the underling into line.

River dolphins and porpoises

The most primitive living dolphins are the river dolphins. They are found in the turbid waters of river systems like the Amazon, the Orinoco, La Plata, the Ganges, the Indus and the Chang Jiang. Their eyesight is poor so they rely almost totally on a highly specialized broad-beam sonar to find their way about and to locate food such as freshwater catfish or crustaceans. They have long snouts and catch their prey in the sharp front teeth, gradually transferring it to the back of the mouth where it is chewed before being swallowed. They are slow swimmers and usually inhabit the quiet sections of rivers where the water is deep and calm. They tend to live a solitary life.

Porpoises, similar in shape to dolphins but without the beak, are to be found in small groups of two or three individuals, or swimming alone. They are smaller than dolphins, generally measuring between 4-6 ft (1.2-1.8 m). These marine mammals often enter harbors or

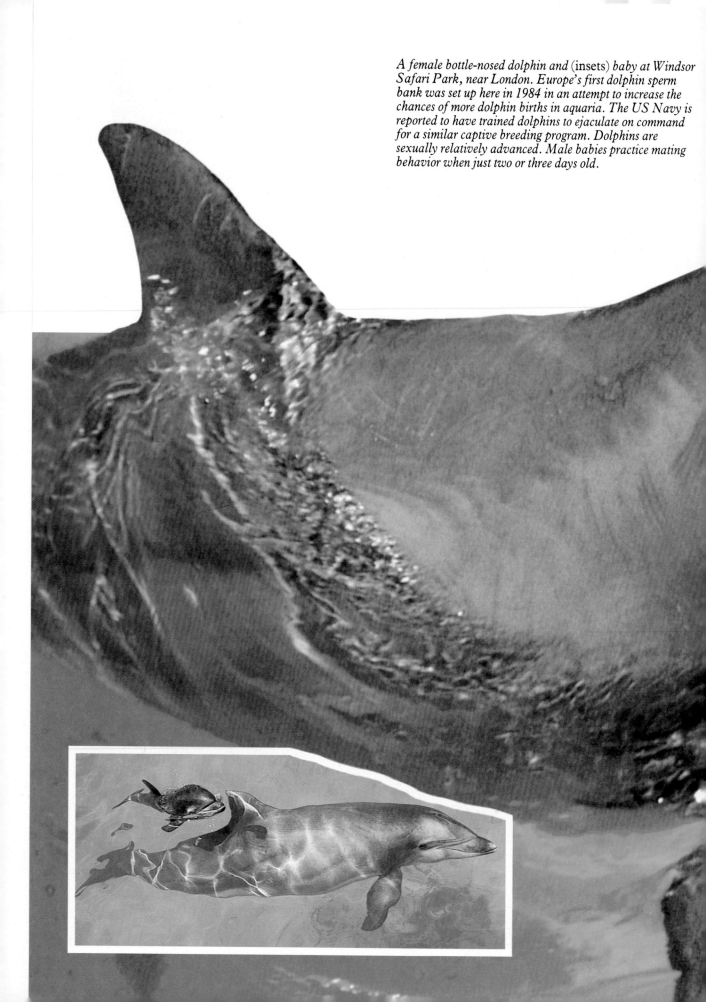

A female bottle-nosed dolphin and (insets) baby at Windsor Safari Park, near London. Europe's first dolphin sperm bank was set up here in 1984 in an attempt to increase the chances of more dolphin births in aquaria. The US Navy is reported to have trained dolphins to ejaculate on command for a similar captive breeding program. Dolphins are sexually relatively advanced. Male babies practice mating behavior when just two or three days old.

The young calf, as the baby dolphin is known, is born tail first. The birth can take up to two hours and so it is of vital importance that the head and blowhole come out last. Once the calf is born the mother quickly swims around it, snapping the umbilical cord, ready to nudge the calf's head up to the surface where it takes its first breath. Calfs do this automatically seconds after birth but the mother is there in case of any difficulties. The calf is roughly a third of her length, 3 ft (1 m) long, and weighs about 25 lbs (11 kg). It is born with its eyes open, can swim perfectly and is agile like its parents. Usually only one calf is born although cases of twins have been reported.

Within 24 hours of the birth the baby takes its first drink of milk, and does so underwater. How it achieves this is ingenious. There are two milk ducts each located beneath grooves towards the dolphin's tail. Since dolphins have solid jaws they can't actually suck the teats. Instead they wrap their tongues around them and

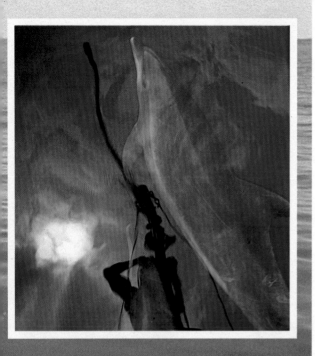

this stimulus prompts the mother to squirt a large volume of milk into their mouths. In this way the calf gets a lot of nourishment quickly, can swim to the surface for air and return to get another "schlug" from the other side. Initially, they feed every twenty minutes.

Dolphins continue to suckle their young for between one-and-a-half and two years, far longer than their human friends, although mixed feeding starts at about the same time — at four or five months. Dolphin milk is conducive to growth, containing six times as much protein as human milk and also far more fat. Drinking its mother's milk a human baby doubles its birth weight in half a year, but a baby dolphin does so in just a couple of months.

The mother, with the help of the other females, protects and assists her young for several weeks, keeping sharks away and also any unfriendly males. After that the young one is on its own, ready to take its place as a member of the herd.

Dolphins gain free rides on the pressure waves at the bows of ships, stop swimming and glide, much like a surfer, to speeds in excess of 35 mph (56 km/h). Common dolphins are the experts. They will ride a bow-wave for hours at a time, one New Zealand animal traveling for 70 miles (113 km) before veering off.

Bottle-nosed dolphins have been seen to "bodysurf" on waves close to the beach, turning back at the last moment before the breaker curls over and crashes onto the shore.

Chapter 3
The Greatest Show on Earth

One of the first marine aquaria to specialize in keeping and training dolphins for public performances was Marineland of Florida at St Augustine. It was set up in 1938 primarily as a studio for underwater films and known as Marine Studios, but very quickly the dolphins took center stage and Marineland became one of the most successful dolphinaria in the world. Millions of people have been entertained there by the tricks and antics of dolphins and small whales.

Surviving in captivity

It was not, however, the first place to exhibit dolphins, for during the nineteenth century many zoos and aquaria in Europe held captive dolphins and porpoises. Some even tried to exhibit whales — belugas or white whales were taken to Britain in 1897, but they died. Indeed, survival in captivity has been a constant and serious problem for dolphinaria. Animals seem to live for a much shorter time than they would in the wild and captive breeding, with the exception of a few key centers, is proving to be difficult. Many zoos and aquaria have been fortunate in having dolphin births, but limited success in getting the young dolphins to survive for very long.

Marineland of Florida established the first breeding group of dolphins. It is composed of bottle-nosed dolphins, the most successful species to breed in captivity. At the Dolphin Breeding Workshop in 1975, it was estimated that 150 baby bottle-nosed dolphins had been born in captivity. The many hundreds of others in oceanaria the world over have been taken from the wild, the main reason that conservationists are very critical of these establishments.

Marineland

However, dolphinaria provided the first and generally the best opportunity of observing dolphin behavior. Marineland of Florida, for instance, pioneered the early work on the sounds that dolphins make for communication and echolocation. Researchers tried to devise a blindfold that would fit a dolphin in order to test the hypothesis that the animal can find its way about without sight, by bouncing sounds off objects. But there were problems. Nothing seemed to stay firmly attached around the dolphin's head or stick to the skin.

Bottle-nosed dolphins "tail-walking" at the Miami Seaquarium. This species is the most commonly found dolphin in captivity, and probably the one possessing the most humor. One dolphin researcher remarked that it "frolics with its mind as well as its body".

step-by-step, building this up to a much more elaborate performance.

Kathy's first blindfold test was to locate a target panel, press a paddle which caused a bell to ring and then return to the researcher for the reward. This she quickly achieved. Underwater microphones in the tank confirmed that Kathy was using sounds to find her way to and from the target, and she could find it when it was only one inch (25 mm) across and she was 35 feet (10.6 m) away. Small pieces of fish, falling in the water, were easily found and hastily gobbled down. A maze of vertically placed rods were negotiated with ease. The blindfolded dolphin did not touch a single rod, even though the configuration of the maze could be changed in an instant.

After the TV show had finished, Kathy was returned to her normal duties of entertaining the huge audiences that marine circuses command. Dolphins have incredible memories for tricks and are amazing mimics. One researcher even had a dolphin mimic human words much like a parrot, and also had it counting up to 10. They are, indeed, first class performers and with that perpetual grin endear themselves to their audience.

Using simple verbal, visual or whistle commands and a fishy tidbit as a reward, a dolphin trainer is able to teach these animals to perform the most amazing tricks. But sometimes a dolphin will refuse to carry out a trick and will sulk or get angry, splashing water over the trainer.

Back flips and feathers

At the Oceanic Institute of Hawaii a dolphin was rewarded when it performed a new trick that it had invented itself. It responded with back-flips, somersaults, splashing, moving in a spiral, and even swam upside down with its tail high in the air. In another tank a pair of dolphins invented a game with a large white feather. They found that if they placed the feather in the current of water from the inlet pipe it would shoot across the pool and they could chase and recover it. Soon, they discovered that if they placed the feather in the eddies to the side of the main current they could beat it across the pool.

Dolphins in captivity can be "moody" and are quick to become bored. Possibly it is just another side of their intelligence. A trainer must be extremely sensitive to these moods for an uncooperative dolphin can be very awkward indeed. Dolphins fed up with repeating a trick over and over again will sulk at the side of the pool or splash the trainer and any other bystander unfortunate enough to be within splashing-distance. And dolphins have their own ideas about their routines. For example,

Below and right: *Dolphins are able to leap 20 ft (6 m) into the air. Their eyesight is as good above as below the water, and they can take a small object from a trainer's mouth with accuracy and ease.*

In addition to their aquabatic skills, dolphins are good mimics. One animal kept and trained in a research laboratory could imitate human speech. It could count up to 10 and almost say a few words in English, although its true skill lay in the speed with which it could copy or mimic.

there is a report from Seaworld in San Diego of a trainer cutting short a killer whale's performance and being dragged by the leg into the water. The crowd rose in horror expecting her to be ripped apart, but there was hardly a scratch on her leg. It was the only way the whale could make its point and protest.

Dominant dolphins

Observers of captive dolphins suggest that a dominance hierarchy exists in dolphin groups, that is, there are dominant and submissive animals in a strict "pecking order". The dominant male in a tank, for instance, prefers to swim at the center or near to the clean water inlet. He also tends to swim alone, occasionally accompanied by a female or younger male. He will sometimes show signs of aggression. When a young male approaches a dominant male's female companion, or heads towards a choice piece of food, the dominant male will see him off with a bite to the body or a slap with the tail, not a damaging challenge if you consider that a dolphin can knock the stuffing out of a shark by ramming it with its snout.

Below: *Pacific white-sided dolphins at San Diego. In the wild they are very active animals, often leaping high into the air. Once, an individual landed on the deck of a research boat and had to be hastily returned to the sea.*

Thousands of white-sided dolphins may travel in a single school. They are distributed widely in the Pacific Ocean, and are sometimes seen with other dolphins and whales.

Bottom and right: *Bottle-nosed dolphins performing.*

At Marineland in Florida, the second highest-ranking dolphin was a female named Pudgy. She was not at all in awe of the dominant male but was instead quite inquisitive about him. If any strange diver entered the tank she viewed him or her as a potential danger, even if he was wearing exactly the same underwater suit and breathing equipment as the regular keeper. Pudgy would inspect him and, providing she judged him to be friendly, would report back to the dominant male who would then, in his turn, venture forward to carry out his own inspection.

Dolphins released back into the wild are often reluctant to go. Those that have lived with humans for any length of time seem to find it difficult to break the ties and fend for themselves once again. Their natural behavior will have undergone substantial modifications and, as a consequence, they actively seek to return to their tank. At Marineland in Florida, for instance, a dolphin was released into the Atlantic but it stayed close to the aquarium site for several weeks before it eventually swam away. A few days later a dolphin was caught not all that far away with extraordinary ease. At the Aquarium of St Petersburg Beach on the Gulf coast

Work and social pressures affect dolphins too. Three dolphins, Aphrodite, Mimi and Kibby, were sent to Florida for rest and recuperation from their stressful life at Baltimore Aquarium. They were not asked to perform tricks and were not involved in a social status battle in their tank, but the gaze of 1 600 000 visitors a year proved too much and they suffered gastric ulcers.

At Batumi dolphinarium, in the USSR, experiments with dolphins have shown that these creatures might be used to locate schools of fish, maintain contact with underwater laboratories and help rescue workers at sea. They are also considering a dolphin dairy farm, since the milk from a Black Sea dolphin contains many times as much fat and protein as does cow's milk.

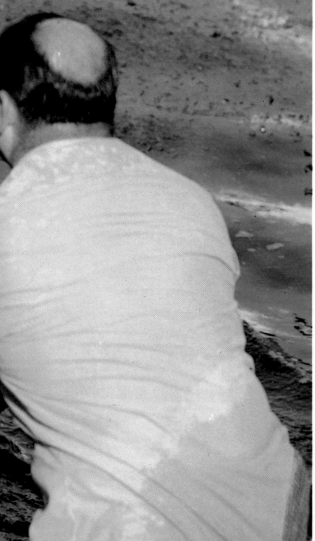

of Florida another newly released dolphin kept turning up in fishing nets in a series of attempts to get back to its tank. The people at the aquarium eventually gave in and let it return, much to the relief of the local fishermen.

Unfortunately dolphins in captivity have suffered illness and even death as a result of acts of violence or just plain stupidity. At the Windsor Safari Park in Britain, for instance, a ball studded with nails was found floating in the dolphin pool. In the same pool a dolphin died after eating a plastic bag.

Dolphins today are valuable animals. Dolphinaria, particularly in the USA, are big business, and the stars do not come cheap — it is not just bottle-nosed dolphins that perform there but also white-sided dolphins, belugas, pilot whales, false killer whales and even enormous killer whales. It has been estimated that many millions of dollars have changed hands in procuring these animals from the wild.

Bottle-nosed dolphins in captivity at the Miami Seaquarium (above), the Oceanarium, Port Elizabeth, South Africa (left), and (inset far left) Whipsnade Zoo, near London.

It is thought that the people of ancient Crete caught and tamed dolphins, and often hung a fish from the prow of their ships to attract a dolphin as pilot. They were also guided to Delphi, sanctuary of Apollo and center of the world, by a dolphin-god. The dolphins of pre-Hellenic Crete were treated as gods, and for centuries later the seafarers of the Mediterranean regarded the presence of dolphins as a good omen for their voyage. When the dolphins disappeared a storm was brewing.

airmen was pushed ashore by dolphins in the Pacific. And in 1966 dolphins fought off sharks and helped a bather reach land in the Gulf of Suez.

Dusky dolphins appear to be particularly concerned about others in distress. There is the story told by the head trainer at a marine circus in New Zealand of a captive dusky responding immediately to a diver pretending to be drowning. The dolphin lifted him up and held him above the surface at the side of the pool. The dolphin also went to the aid of the sick baby of a common dolphin in the same tank.

Military uses

It is well known that dolphins help each other. There are many cases recorded of dolphins supporting a sick or injured companion, keeping its head at the surface so that it can breathe. There is even a tale from Russian fishermen of a group of dolphins protecting a seal from a pack of marauding killer whales. Dolphins have been reported to bite harpoon lines in order to release a speared individual, and even to charge boats when one of their number has been caught.

It is thought that at one time military spy satellites were used not only for spotting rocket silos but also to find dolphin pools, for these marine creatures have come under close scrutiny from military designers and engineers. The tail section of dolphins has been tried as a method of propulsion for a ship and has been found to be far more efficient than the traditional propellor. Naval architects have spent long hours studying the hydrodynamics of dolphins in order to apply them to new submarine designs.

The US Navy has been training dolphins and pilot whales to recover warheads and other military equipment lost on the bottom of the sea. It is generally known that naval authorities of several countries are currently, or have in the past, trained dolphins to fix explosives to the hulls of enemy vessels, to discover or destroy enemy mines, or to help detect the presence of enemy submarines. If they can be trained to do that, it is not a far stretch of the imagination to consider them in front-line attacks, perhaps exploding underwater mines — and killing themselves in the process — or guarding harbor entrances against enemy frogmen.

But since for each nation military research is a

Dolphins involved in military activities are trained to live freely in the sea yet return to their base on the command of their trainer. Tuffy, a bottle-nosed dolphin, was trained to liaise between laboratories on the sea floor, Sealabs II and III, and their surface ship. He also guided lost divers back to their submarine bases.

Top and left: A Dall's porpoise trapped in the net of a "superseiner" (above) out to catch tuna. The biggest threats to this species, though, are the salmon drift nets of the Japanese Salmon Fisheries Cooperative that operates, under permit, inside the US Fisheries Conservation Zone, and is allowed an "accidental" take of over 5000 dolphins.

top-secret operation, there is little information available. For example, it is known that at the end of the Vietnam War the US brought back some dolphins which they had out there, but it is uncertain what part they had played in the hostilities. Public outcry has certainly deterred the use of such peaceful animals for naval warfare, but it may be that experiments continue, only now with still greater secrecy...

Pelorus Jack

In many parts of the world there have been reports of dolphins turning up at the same place time and time again, and having a special affinity for man. Such a dolphin was Pelorus Jack, a Risso's dolphin that lived in the Cook Strait between the North and South Islands of New Zealand. Jack would greet steamships and leap about in front of the bows, seemingly guiding them

through the strait. The dolphin became a tourist attraction, and the New Zealand government passed a Special Order in Council making it illegal "to take fish or mammal, commonly known as Risso's dolphin, in the waters of Cook Strait".

Fishes Royal

Dolphins can be found all around the British Isles. However, any that are actually caught in British waters belong to the ruling monarch. An act, passed in 1320, states that dolphins, whales and sturgeons must be offered for the Royal Table or allowed to swim free in the seas. Even an injured animal that has been patched up at an animal hospital must be given its freedom when fully recovered. It is breaking the law to keep a dolphin caught in the wild around Britain without special permission from the Crown.

Gone fishing

Between Cape Blanc and Cape Timiris, on the Mauritanian coast, the Imragen peoples follow the migration of huge shoals of mullet. They catch the fish with the help of dolphins. The fishermen watch as the dolphins appear on the horizon and as they get closer to the shore nets are placed out in the shallows. The dolphins drive the mullet into the nets, grab as many fish as they can swallow, sometimes diving between and around the legs of the fishermen, and then leave. The Imragen likewise haul out their share of the spoils and leave the fish to dry in the sun, to be eaten later during the leaner parts of the year. To the Imragen the dolphin is a sacred animal.

Whistling for help

In Burma there are similar tales of cooperation between dolphin and man, with reports of several villages having their own local marine friend. On the Tepegos River in South America, one explorer discovered a fisherman who would tap the side of his boat with an oar and whistle a strange tune to summon an Amazon river dolphin. The fisherman in his boat would drive the fish shoal to the river bank while the dolphin frightened them to the surface where they could be picked off quite easily by man and dolphin alike.

And as long ago as the first century AD Pliny the Elder wrote about French fishermen using dolphins to find shoals of fish. These fortunate dolphins were rewarded not only with a share of the catch, but also with pieces of bread dipped in red wine.

Right and below right: The slaughter at Iki. A thousand or more dolphins are herded into the harbor at Katsumoto and killed because the local fishermen believe that their livelihoods are threatened by the dolphins eating or chasing away the fish. Conservationists world-wide have condemned this slaughter.

One American released a herd of dolphins the fishermen had trapped and received a suspended prison sentence.

Below: A bottle-nosed dolphin stands up in the water.

Left: *A common porpoise washed ashore.*
Below: *At Izu 6000 dolphins were slaughtered in 1979 to supply the* teriyaki *market, but by 1980 the price dropped by a third and the killing was reduced when environmentalists revealed that the meat was contaminated with 10 times the level of mercury allowed for human consumption.*

Unnecessary slaughter

Yet, despite all this seemingly intelligent cooperative behavior, dolphins are caught and killed by man in their thousands. Dolphins in the Pacific Ocean, for example, swim with the tuna — the same tuna that ends up on your supermarket shelf. The fishermen spot the tuna shoals by looking out for the leaping dolphins. The tuna are caught by surrounding them in enormous nets, known as purse-seine nets. As the circle of the net is drawn in, not only are the fish caught, but the dolphins are trapped as well.

Legislation has been introduced in the USA to minimize the number of dolphins killed. It decrees that when nets are hauled in, one side must be temporarily slackened to let the dolphins escape over the top. Another law passed in 1972 forbids the capturing or importing of marine mammals into the US. Similarly products made from marine mammals are forbidden. Nevertheless 40 000 dolphins are still killed each year.

Perhaps the greatest slaughter has been around the Japanese island of Iki, where the fishermen feel that the dolphins are competing with them for fish. Thousands

have been trapped, hauled by their tails from the water, and knifed or clubbed to death, only to be fed into a grinding and mincing machine to be turned into pig-fodder. Iki Bay turns red with their blood.

The Japanese authorities tried to frighten the dolphins from the area with the help of an artificial killer whale that emitted noises thought to be scary, but the dolphins weren't fooled and played with the device. Unfortunately their intelligence, in this case, cost them their lives.

A diver appearing to be in distress receives playful assistance from a dolphin. Wild dolphins, particularly bottle-nosed dolphins, sometimes come close inshore and frolic with fishermen and bathers. They have even been known to nudge a swimmer in difficulty towards the safety of the beach. Why they should be so friendly to man, and overcome the natural urge to be wary of us, is still a mystery to scientists.

There are many instances of dolphins appearing off bathing beaches and swimming with holidaymakers. One such bottle-nosed dolphin appeared in various places around the British coast and gained a new name in every port: Donald in the Isle of Man, Bubbles off the coast of Wales, and Beaky along the south Cornwall coast!

GUIDE TO ASSISTING STRANDED DOLPHINS

● Keep the skin moist. Dolphins breathe air and so can survive for a time (several hours) out of water as long as their skin does not dry out.

● If a dolphin is exhausted, don't put it into deep water as it may not be able to swim and consequently will drown. Support it instead in shallow water with the blowhole just covered, allowing the animal to bend its head up to breathe. Although dolphins attain a considerable weight, some up to 800 lbs (360 kg), it does not require phenomenal strength to do this.

● When several are stranded together, moving one back into the water at a time will not work. It will instinctively return to join its stranded companions. The solution is to summon enough help to move them all back into the water at the same time. If this is impossible, try moving some higher on the beach and then move one out into the water. If its fellows are sufficiently far away, their whistles of distress won't travel through the water summoning the rescued one back. You can then move the others down one at a time.

● You will have to handle dolphins firmly but try to be gentle. They do not like having their flippers yanked but these, and their tail flukes, are really all you can get a grip on when attempting to move them. Nevertheless try to keep the dolphin calm. It is more likely to die from struggling than from being out of the water. But remember, keep its skin wet at all times.

The sad sight of stranded dolphins. In life, they are remarkable sea creatures. Plutarch, in the first century AD, wrote: "To the dolphin alone nature has given that which the best philosophers seek: friendship for no advantage. Though it has no need of help of any man, yet it is a genial friend to all, and has helped man."

PICTURE CREDITS